CHINA CLAY

–

A GEOLOGIST'S VIEW

Colin Bristow

GEOLOGY OF CHINA CLAY

- Origin

- Minerals

- Environment

- World occurrence

© Colin Bristow, formerly Chief Geologist, English China Clays

Publishers details: First published 2006   ISBN 1 900147 459

Designed by Fergie
Lelant, Cornwall TR26 3LL

Printed by
Short Run Press
Exeter, Devon EX2 7LW

Cover picture – China clay monitor working in Goonbarrow pit with face behind show-ing steeply inclined quartz-tourmaline veins set in kaolinized granite. Boulders of vein material and unkaolinized granite (stent) cloak the upper part of the face.

CONTENTS:

View down the Fal Valley with Wheal Remfry china clay pit in the foreground.

The unique landscape created by the china clay industry around St Austell and in other parts of Cornwall and southwest Devon prompts visitor and local person alike to ask some simple questions:

What is china clay?

How was china clay formed?

What minerals and rocks are found in china clay pits?

How are deposits of china clay found?

How about the environmental impact?

Are there other china clay deposits in the rest of the world?

What about the future?

This booklet aims to provide some answers to these questions.

INTRODUCTION

The massive occurrences of china clay in Cornwall and Devon are unique, in terms of their combination of quantity and quality, in the world. China clay production has been, for the last 150 years, the most important engine driving the Cornish economy, providing employment to generations of Cornishmen; it also represents the latest stage in a long Cornish mining tradition going back some 3000 years.

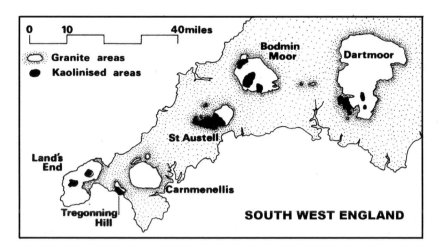

Figure 1 *The granite masses of South-west England.*

All the granites of Southwest England, with the exception of the Isles of Scilly and Lundy granites, are known to contain some china clay, formed by the process of kaolinization **(Figure 1)**. The St. Austell granite contains the greatest concentration of china clay workings, more particularly in the western part of the granite mass. The southwestern part of the Dartmoor granite, around Lee Moor, also contains some important china clay deposits, which are extensively worked. Deposits on Bodmin Moor at Stannon and Parson's Park and in the Land's End granite at Bostraze were worked until recently. There is also some china clay in the Tregonning granite, near Helston. This is where Cookworthy made his original discovery of china clay in the mid-18th century, but it has not been worked for nearly 100 years.

Since china clay was first produced for commercial use late in the eighteenth century, around 170 million tonnes have been produced from Cornwall and Devon. This would be worth, at present prices for china clay, around £15 billion. China clay is Britain's second most important mineral export, after petroleum, and it is sent all over the world for use in a great variety of industries such as paper, ceramics, paint, plastics, metal casting and medicines. Further resources of china clay await exploitation and prospecting has not yet fully defined the limits of all the deposits.

Figure 2 *Wheal Martyn china clay pit in 2005. The captain, Paddy Bristow, sets out on a tour of inspection. Note the monitor working on the far side of the pit and an excavator removing rock on the right. The clay stream from the monitor is flowing to the sump on the left from where it will be pumped up to classifiers, which will remove the sand.*

The extraction of china clay has ceated a unique landscape, with massive tips of waste sand and deep water-filled pits, which we are now beginning to appreciate has the potential for exceptional biodiversity, with many unusual habitats being colonised by rare plants. In parallel with the natural revegetation, a big programme of managed environmental restoration in Britain is well on the way to creating one of the largest areas of lowland heath in the country.

The china clay pits **(Figure 2)** also offer a fantastic window into the geology, with their magnificent faces of rock showing how the process of converting solid granite into china clay took place; as well as helping us to understand the processes of mineral formation which led to the creation of metalliferous deposits such as tin and copper. Many research projects by Universities, both in the U.K. and overseas, have contributed to this understanding, and a steady flow of field trips enables students and others interested in geology to study the processes of mineral formation.

At Wheal Martyn a 'Boulder Park' has been created to show examples of some interesting hard rocks found in china clay pits around St Austell **(Figure 3)**. These are listed in the Appendix and referred to in the text of this booklet.

Figure 3 *Two young visitors examine the boulder of Wheal Remfry breccia in the Boulder Park at Wheal Martyn Museum, February 2006.*

WHAT IS CHINA CLAY?

China clay was formed by the alteration in situ of a mineral called feldspar, one of the principal components of granite, into a new mineral called kaolinite. Outside Britain china clay deposits are referred to as 'kaolin deposits' and the name originates from a Chinese location called 'kauling', meaning the high ridge. The clay for making the finest Chinese porcelain, made as early as A.D. 800, came from this area, which is just south of the Yangtse river in present-day Kiangsi Province.

Kaolinite – the main mineral forming china clay

Kaolinite is the main constituent of china clay; it always crystallises in a fine grained form, unlike the quartz, mica or feldspar in granite, which usually form large crystals visible to the naked eye. The crystals of kaolinite are measured in microns, a micron being one thousandth of a millimetre. Typically kaolinite crystals are 1-10 microns in size, there are also large kaolinite crystals up to 100 microns in diameter, or one-tenth of a millimetre **(Figures 4 and 20)**. Electron microscopes are capable of magnifying the kaolinite crystals, showing they consist of stacks of plates, approximately hexagonal in shape. The platy nature of kaolinite is due to its crystal structure and provides one of the fundamentally important commercial properties of the mineral for, in a suspension of water, the plates easily slide over one another, like a pack of cards, to give good flow chacteristics. Kaolinite is a hydrated aluminium silicate ($Si_4Al_4O_{10}(OH)_8$) or, in terms of oxides, it is SiO_2 46.5%, Al_2O_3 39.5% and H_2O 14%.

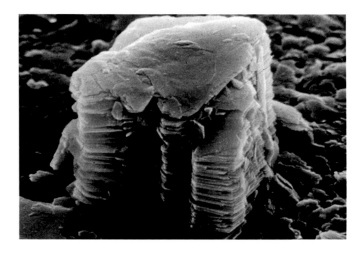

Figure 4 *Scanning electron microscope photograph of a large kaolinite crystal, magnified about 10,000 times.*

A single plate of kaolinite is composed of two sheets: an octahedral sheet containing aluminium, oxygen and hydrogen atoms and a tetrahedral sheet composed of silicon and oxygen atoms **(Figure 5)**. The crystal structure of kaolinite is resistant to attack by most corrosive fluids and can therefore be regarded as an inert white powder, which will not react with most mediums in which it is placed, another important commercial property.

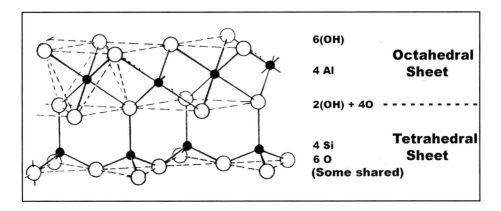

Figure 5 *The crystal structure of the kaolinite lattice – see text*

Kaolinite is a member of the group of minerals known as 'clay minerals', other members of this group include halloysite which has a similar composition to kaolinite, but occurs rolled up like minature parchment scrolls. Kaolinite has the simplest kind of structure, other clay minerals have more complex layer structures. Illite is a kind of fine grained mica and smectite has the property of expanding when wetted and absorbing fluids. Most people will be familiar with this clay mineral in the form of cat litter.

Kaolinite is also the predominant constituent of 'ball clay', a plastic sedimentary clay extensively worked at Bovey and Petrockstow in Devon and Wareham in Dorset. Ball clay is an invaluable material for all kinds of ceramics, because of its ability to fire white and impart plasticity and strength to an unfired ceramic body. Ball clays originated from the weathering of a variety of rock types under sub-tropical conditions. This soft weathered material was then eroded and transported by rivers to be laid down on flood plains and in lakes in Tertiary times (about 35 million years ago) to form seams in fault-formed basins. Ball clay kaolinite is always finer grained than china clay kaolinite and the layer structure is less well ordered. Most ball clays are usually darker coloured than china clays, due to the presence of dark coloured coaly (lignitic) material, this burns out when the ceramic article is fired to give a near-white product. Clays similar to ball clays also occur all over the world.

CORNISH GEOLOGY

Many of the rocks seen around the coast of Cornwall are hardened muds, silts and sands laid down in a sea which wholly or partly covered what is now Cornwall during the Devonian and Carboniferous geological periods, from about 400 to 300 million years ago. Volcanic activity occurred in this tectonically unstable area from time to time, producing lava flows and volcanic ashes and minor intrusions of magma below the sea bed, which we call 'greenstones'.

At this time Cornwall lay near the Equator and was situated between two gigantic supercontinents. The southern supercontinent, called Gondwana, lay in the southern hemisphere and included Africa, Antarctica, Australia, South America and India. It was slowly moving northwards and, over a period of about 50 million years, gradually collided with the southern margin of the northern supercontinent which included North America, Greenland, Scandanavia, northern Europe, Siberia and most of Britain. Cornwall lay in the northern part of the collision zone. Geologists call this collision event the Variscan Orogeny, and the sediments and volcanic rocks which had been laid down in the sea between the two tectonic plates were compressed and buckled into folds **(Figure 6)**, with extensive faulting. The crumpled rocks on the site of the collision piled up to produce a mighty mountain chain which extended all the way from Poland to Alabama (the Atlantic Ocean opened up later). Mountain chains are a bit like

Figure 6 *Folded Devonian slaty mudstones, Porthleven, penknife for scale.*

icebergs; the part that sticks up above the surface is much less than the massive root pushed down into the hot plastic rocks of the mantle below the crust, to depths of perhaps as much as 40 km. At this depth heating began to 'cook' (metamorphose) the original clay minerals, forming anhydrous minerals and releasing water. At greater temperatures some of the less refractory minerals began to melt and the resulting fluid collected to form a mass of molten magma. Gradually these 'bubbles' of molten magma coalesced to form large masses many kilometres across.

At these sort of depths, the rocks are so hot that they can yield by plastic deformation. So, as the granite magma was slightly lighter than the surrounding rocks, it began to rise up through the overlying pile of sedimentary rocks forming the mountain chain, rather like a gigantic hot air balloon in very slow motion. Repeatedly magma welled up into the core of the mountain chain in a series of pulses spread over 30 million years. It came up to perhaps 3-5 km below the land surface at the time and then began to cool and crystallize, to become the granite masses we see today forming the spine of the Cornubian peninsula **(Figure 2, p. 2)**. A fuller explanation of the events in Cornwall 400-300 years ago will be found in 'Cornwall's Geology and Scenery' (see list of publications at the end of this booklet).

The earliest granites were Carnmenellis and Bodmin Moor **(Figures 1 and 7)**, intruded about 290 million years ago, right at the end of the Carboniferous Period. The later granites are those of Land's End and St Austell, intruded in the early part of the Permian Period. The St Austell granite is a particularly complex granite made up of a series of intrusions intruded one after the other between 285 and 270 million years ago, with the oldest in the east around Luxulyan and the youngest in the west in the Nanpean/Fal Valley areas **(Figure 8)**.

Much of the younger granite in the western part of the St Austell mass (Boulders 2, 3, 4 and 5 in Wheal Martyn Boulder Park) is unusual, because a lithium-containing mica takes the place of the more normal biotite mica (Boulder No. 1 at Wheal Martyn is biotite granite). This is important, because biotite releases iron oxide during kaolinization, colouring the resulting china clay red, yellow or brown, which is commercially undesirable, as one of the most important properties of china clay is whiteness. So the lithium mica granites of the western part of the St Austell granite, with little or no biotite, are good parents for china clay.

At a late stage in the crystallization process, fluids separated out which gave rise to veins of very coarsely crystalline material, which is known as 'pegmatite' (Boulder No. 6 at Wheal Martyn Boulder Park). Many pegmatites have formed at the margin of an intrusion where a younger phase has been intruded against an older phase; these are known as 'stockscheider' pegmatites. Boulder No. 6 at Wheal Martyn is one of these **(Figure 9)**. Pegmatites have, in

Figure 7 *The Cheesewring, Bodmin Moor. A superb example of a granite tor.*

the past, been worked as a source of feldspar for ceramics and glassmaking, as at Trezaise and Kernick. Trezaise is now a County Geological Site and can be visited (Grid reference SW 996586).

A final stage of granite magma intrusion, about 5-10 million years after the main granite moved into place, is represented by the elvans, which are narrow (2-10m wide) vertical 'dykes' **(Figure 10)**, formed by granitic magma being squirted up steeply inclined cracks and cooling relatively rapidly, so that they are narrow (2-10m wide) vertical 'dykes' **(Figure 10)**,

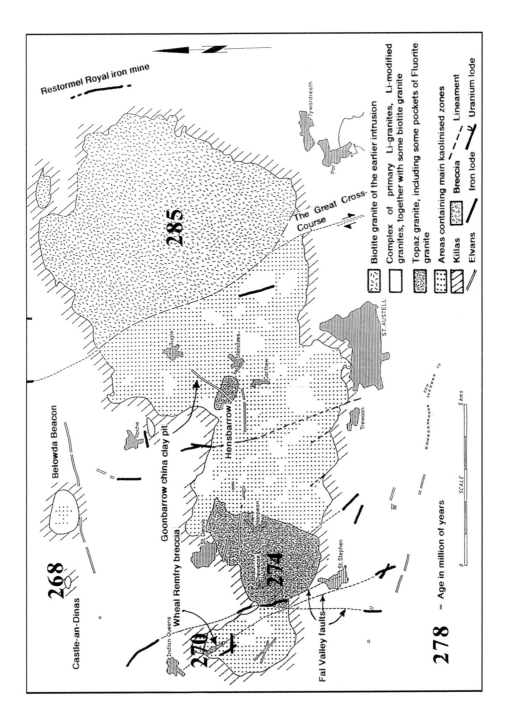

Figure 8 *Geological map of the St Austell granite, showing some of the locations mentioned in the text. Partly based on the 1:50,000 Sheet 347, published by the British Geological Survey (NERC copyright reserved).*

Figure 9 (Left) *Pegmatite boulder in Wheal Martyn china clay pit (before removal to Wheal Martyn Boulder Park).*

Figure 10 (Below) *An elvan dyke in Wheal Remfry china clay pit. This type of dyke was produced by an injection of granite magma up a subvertical crack. As the elvan cooled quickly, the crystals are very fine grained and may originally have been in part glass, particularly at the margins.*

much finer grained than a normal granite (Boulder 7 at Wheal Martyn). Some of these elvans, such as one that occurs in the cliffs just north of Pentewan, are suitable for carving and were much used by medieval masons **(Figure 11)**. Generally the best elvans for building stone are found away from the granites where the elvan intrudes the sedimentary slaty rocks.

Some of the granite magma probably reached the surface in the rapidly eroding mountain range and formed volcanoes. Nearly all of this volcanic material has since been removed by erosion, but a small downfaulted patch occurs in SE Cornwall at Kingsand, where a small area of sediments is also seen, showing that the climate was hot and arid at the time the granites were moving into place. Fossil animal burrows in the sediments show that there was some life at the time, perhaps they were made by primitive burrowing mammal-like reptiles which were our 160-million-greats grandparents!

Figure 11 *A sermon in stone carved in Pentewan Stone (elvan) by medieval masons on St Austell Church tower.*

One very important property of the granites in southwest England is that they have an unusually high content of radioactive elements, such as uranium and thorium. **Figure 25** (p. 28) shows a highly magnified flake of biotite mica from Boulder 1 at Wheal Martyn, the black spots are caused by radiation from minute specks of radioactive mineral altering the mica. These radioactive elements not only release radioactivity, but also heat. For this reason, the Cornish granites are known as high heat producing (HHP) granites. Computer modelling shows that this radiogenic heat would have caused the cooling to have been much slower than it would have been for a granite with a more normal content of radioactive elements so, even today, the granites of South-west England are slightly warmer than the surrounding sedimentary rocks.

Heat from the slowly cooling granites sweated out metals from the rocks of the mountain range and the granites themselves so that, as the granite cooled, minerals containing these metals crystallised in cracks around the granite masses to form the tin and copper bearing mineral lodes which were exploited until recently in Cornwall. In the 270 million years since the granite was intruded, the Variscan mountain range has been gradually worn down to become the comparatively gentle landscape of today. Cornwall was probably submerged beneath the sea on a couple of occasions, but during much of this period Cornwall was an island or a peninsula like today, with a humid tropical or sub-tropical climate. This kind of climate created intense chemical weathering, which also probably contributed to the formation of the china clay deposits we see today.

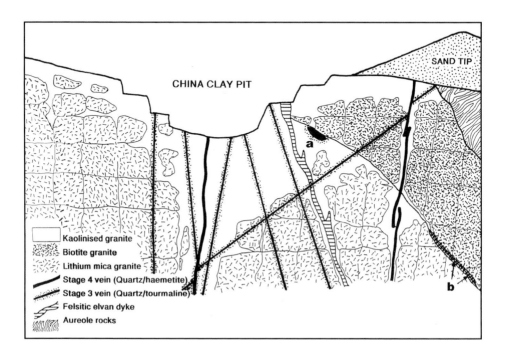

HOW CHINA CLAY DEPOSITS WERE FORMED

Now equipped with an understanding of the greater geological picture, we can return to look in more detail at the actual processes which formed china clay. The process which converted the hard granite into the soft matrix seen in china clay pits is known as 'kaolinization' and involves a whole series of alteration processes caused by different types of water based fluids circulating in the granite. Without exactly the right sequence of altering fluids, china clay deposits on the scale of St Austell would not have formed.

Kaolinization

Unaltered granite is composed of three minerals – quartz, feldspar and mica (see p. 57, boulders 1-5 at Wheal Martyn and **Figure 23** p. 27). Kaolinization does not affect the quartz, which remains relatively unchanged; the white tips of the china clay areas are largely composed of waste quartz sand. The mica initially loses any iron it may have contained to either remain as a colourless mica, or it recrystallizes into a finer grained form. Under prolonged kaolinizing conditions kaolinite can grow between the layers of mica to form the large curled stacks seen in **Figure 20,** p. 25). However, the feldspars in the granite are chemically more reactive and, by a series of stages, were largely transformed into kaolinite. The soda feldspar (plagioclase) is usually the most susceptible, with the more resistant potash feldspar (orthoclase) being less susceptible. Soda feldspar transforms into almost pure kaolinite, whilst potash feldspar changes into a mixture of kaolinite and a kind of fine grained mica called illite. Essentially the chemistry of the process involves the removal of the soluble alkaline hydroxides of sodium and potassium, together with some silica (SiO_2), which is then replaced by water, as in the formula below:

$$2NaAlSi_3O_8 + 3H_2O = Al_2Si_2O_5(OH)_4 + 4SiO_2 + 2NaOH$$

feldspar   water   kaolinite   silica   alkali

Some 25% by weight of the granite is removed during the process of kaolinization, largely by being carried away in solution.

The kaolinized zones are often in the form of funnels, opening out towards the surface and descending to depths of over 100 metres **(Figures 12 and 33,** p. 37). The best quality clay is usually found in the centre of the funnel; there

Figure 12 (opposite) *Generalized section through a typical china clay pit. Any tin or tungsten mineralization would occur in the Stage 3 quartz-tourmaline veins; greisening and tourmalinization associated with these veins is indicated by stippling. a = borosilicate segregation, b = 'stockscheider' pegmatite.*

may be a layer of surface-stained clay underlying the overburden. Sometimes the kaolinized zone takes the form of a cluster of funnels and sometimes it forms a trough-like feature, which may be inclined so that the kaolinized zone dips steeply into the ground at an angle. In some cases unkaolinized granite has been found to overlie kaolinized granite and the explanation for this is usually that the underlying granite is more susceptible to kaolinization; for example by having a higher soda-feldspar content. Occasionally the kaolinized granite is found to be overlain by the sedimentary rocks surrounding the granite ('killas'), which are usually extensively altered by the baking effect when the granite moved into place and by chemical changes brought about by fluids migrating out of the cooling granite. The commonest change is tourmalinization, where the sedimentary rocks are converted by boron-rich fluids to a mixture of quartz and the boron-containing mineral tourmaline to form a striking striped black and white rock.

The various events and alteration processes which have led to the formation of the china clay deposits in the St Austell granite form a series of distinct stages (Ma = millions of years ago):

Stage 1 (285 Ma, 600°C) Molten granite magma moves into place to form the biotite granite forming the eastern part of the St Austell granite intrusion.

Stage 2 (275 Ma, 600°C) A series of pulses of molten magma move into place to form the various lithium- and biotite-granites of the western part of the St Austell granite.

Stage 3 (275-260 Ma, 450-380°C) Formation of sheeted quartz-tourmaline vein systems (Stage 3a) with associated tourmalinization and greisening. Mainstage Mineralisation with more quartz-tourmaline veins and tin- and copper-bearing veins (Stage 3b). Intrusion of elvans up cracks (Stage 3c).

Stage 4 (240 Ma, 350-250°C) 'Cross-course' quartz veins (see p.23) formed with associated further alteration of granite, some clay formed (no kaolinite), formation of iron veins.

Stage 5 (200-25 Ma, 200-30°C) Vigorous radiogenically driven convective circulation draws surface water down into the granite, causing kaolinization. Interrupted on at least two occasions when peninsula was submerged below sea.

Stage 6 (180-25 Ma, 20-50°C) Tropical climate causes deep chemical weathering.

Following the intrusion and initial cooling of the granites **(Stages 1 & 2)**, extensive alteration by circulating fluids took place **(Stage 3)**. Initially the cooling granite provided the main heat source and, as it slowly crystallized, a residual hot water-based fluid separated out, which was rich in elements such as silicon, boron, fluorine and iron. (**Figure 13** – top, Earliest Permian, **Stage 3a**).

14

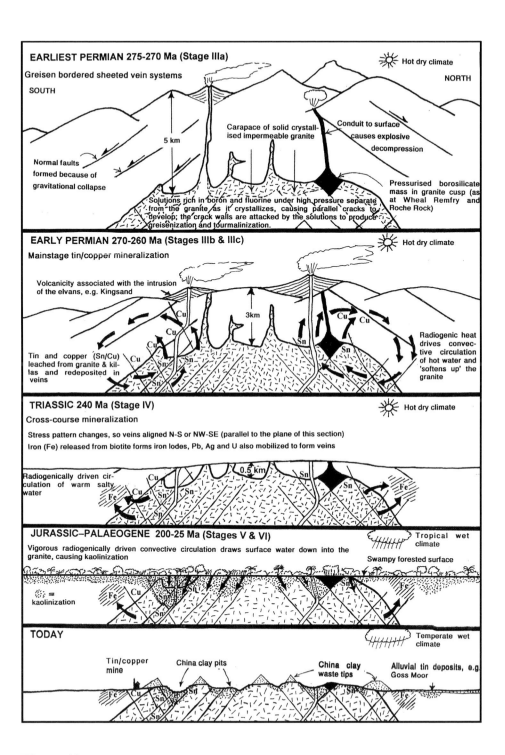

Figure 13 *Diagrammatic series of sections through the St Austell granite showing how the china clay and metalliferous deposits were formed. See text for details.*

As the crystals of the granite crystallized beneath a solid and relatively imperme-able carapace of already crystallized granite, a residual hot watery fluid under very high pressure developed, rather like in a domestic pressure cooker. This fluid was under such high pressure that it caused the crystallizing granite to form a series of parallel cracks perpendicular to the direction of least confining pres-sure. The hot fluid circulated through these cracks to form sheeted vein systems **(Figures 14A and 14B,** pp. 17 and 18), seen in most china clay pits. If you look down into the active Wheal Martyn pit from the Observation Platform, you will see these vein systems looking like a series of parallel black lines.

These reactive fluids containing silicon, boron, fluorine and iron also al-tered the granite alongside the veins **(Figures 14B,** p. 18**)** by either: (a) replacing the feldspar in the granite with a mixture of quartz and mica (greisening) or, (b) by causing tourmaline to replace some or all of the granite minerals (tourmali-nization). Basically greisening is a process involving the addition of silica and tourmalinization is a process where boron is added. Occasionally a whole mass of granite became 'waterlogged' with these altering fluids, so that large irregular-ly shaped masses of greisen developed, often with much tourmaline. This really is a case of the hot granite stewing in its own juice.

In many china clay pits 'blobs' composed of tourmaline and quartz are found 'floating' in the granite; these range in size from a gooseberry to massive occurrences a hundred metres or more across. It very much looks as if these are segregations of a separate borosilicate fluid. This is well seen in Wheal Remfry china clay pit. Boulder 10 at Wheal Martyn Boulder Park represents this kind of material. It is still controversial, but many now believe that these borosilicate segregations were immiscible with the surrounding granite (oil and water are im-miscible, i.e. they will not mix). Remember the two fluids in a lava lamp!

At Wheal Remfry something even more remarkable seems to have hap-pened to one of these large borosilicate masses. Here, a large mass about 500m long and up to 100m wide had accumulated along a line of weakness caused by one of the faults belonging to the Fal Valley Fault Zone. It appears that it was under considerable pressure and that the borosilicate fluid somehow managed to establish a conduit to the land surface, perhaps triggered by an earthquake, causing it, accompanied by some granite magma, to rush up towards the surface, rather like champagne rushing out of the bottle as the cork pops. Once the pres-sure had been dissipated a lot of the material which had rushed up the conduit fell back down again, and set solid as a mass of granite and killas fragments in a fine-grained matrix of tourmaline and quartz. This dramatic looking rock (**Figure 15,** p.19 and Boulder 9 at the Wheal Martyn Boulder Park), is known as Wheal Remfry breccia, dated at 270 million years ago. Another place where there was an accumulation of borosilicate material was Roche Rock **(Figure 16**, p. 20). However, here there was no explosive decompression, so the borosilicate quietly

Figure 14 *Various types of quartz tourmaline vein:*
14A *Professor Peter Scott admiring a typical sheeted vein system composed of thin quartz-tourmaline veins in Goonbarrow pit. Two sets of veins are seen: one near vertical and one steeply dipping to the left. This indicates that the stress directions in the cooling granite changed between the formation of the two sets of veins. There is only limited greisening alongside the veins.*

Figure 14 *Various types of quartz tourmaline vein (continued):*

14B (Top) *Two parallel gently dipping veins in Goonbarrow pit, forming part of a sheeted vein system, set in white kaolinized granite. The actual crack along which the altering fluid moved is indicated by the thin vein in the centre of the dark coloured mass (best seen in the upper one). On either side of this vein the granite has been altered to a dark material by a process known as 'greisening', whereby the feldspar in the granite is altered to fine quartz and mica. As there is no feldspar left for the later process of kaolinization to alter, the greisen forms a hard rocky material known as 'stent' (see cover).*

14C (Bottom) *A complex quartz-tourmaline vein zone in Rocks china clay pit. This is typical of the veins formed during the Mainstage Mineralisation. Several phases of vein formation can be seen; on the left broken fragments of earlier formed vein indicate some fault movement took place while the vein was forming. Boulder 8 at Wheal Martyn Boulder Park is this type of complex vein.*

Figure 15 *Wheal Remfry breccia; produced by a cataclysmic explosion 270 million years ago. Pale coloured granite and killas fragments are set in a dark matrix of tourmaline and quartz, probably formed by the explosive depressurization of a boro-silicate mass which had accumulated along one of the fault planes belonging to the Fal Valley fault zone.*

crystallized to form a medium grained mixture of quartz and tourmaline usually referred to as 'schorl-rock', now forming a very striking tor-like mass just south of Roche village.

Later in the Early Permian conditions changed and water was drawn into the granite from it's surroundings and a convective circulation of water-based fluids became established in and around the granite, driven by radiogenic heat and residual heat from the cooling granite (**Figure 13** – Early Permian, Stage 3b, p. 15).

Metals such as tin and copper were now leached by these hot fluids from the granite itself and the killas around the granite. As the circulating water reached cooler locations, quartz, tourmaline and metalliferous minerals were precipitated in cracks to form the mineral-bearing veins worked by the tin and copper mines associated with the St Austell granite. This is usually referred to as the 'Main-stage Mineralization'. Fault movement along the line of the vein is common, breaking up the material in the vein **Figure 14C,** p. 18). A quartz-tourmaline vein from Wheal Martyn pit forms Boulder No. 8 in the Wheal Martyn Boulder Park and is typical of the veins formed during the Mainstage mineralization. The mineralizing fluids were quite hot and salty, so it is unlikely that much clay was formed at this early stage, although it is quite likely that the fluids had the effect of 'softening up' the granite and making it more permeable, so that later fluids could more easily penetrate into the mass of the granite. As the granites were intruded in a series of pulses spread over many millions of years, it is often found that the veining formed by different pulses and different stages is superimposed, making the interpretation of the sequence of vein formation in a china clay pit difficult to unravel.

The elvan dykes **(Figure 13** – Early Permian, Stage 3c, p. 15), already discussed above (**Figure 10**, p. 10), were formed by granite magma from the still-molten reservoir at depth rushing up cracks at about the same time as the Mainstage Mineralization, this contributed a further pulse of heat. Boulder No. 7 at Wheal Martyn is a specimen of the Wheal Remfry elvan.

Figure 16 *Roche rock, a borosilicate mass in an outlying cusp of the granite, which quietly crystallized – unlike Wheal Remfry. This 'schorl-rock' is composed of just two minerals: quartz and tourmaline. A 15th century chapel, surmounts the rock.*

The Mainstage Mineralization created the metalliferous veins which were worked in the many important mines in and around the St Austell granite. Not only tin and copper ores were extracted, but other metal ores such as those of tungsten, zinc, silver, nickel, uranium etc. The heyday of metal mining was in the late 18th and early 19th centuries. Bunny and Beam underground tin mines **(Figure 17)** and the famous Carclaze open pit tin mine **(Figure 19)** were all within a few miles of the Museum. Carclaze was worked for tin from ancient times up to the middle of the 19th century and was regarded as one of the 'must see' sites for travellers to Cornwall in the late 18th and early 19th centuries. At that time the china clay was washed away to waste through an adit under the pit bottom. As the 19th century progressed china clay became more important and by 1900 was

Figure 17 *Beam tin mine, remains of a shaft, in Goonbarrow china clay pit. Note the extensive timbering due to the soft ground. Cassiterite (Sn O₂) is the ore of tin. The specimen shown in **Figure 30**, p. 31 came from here.*

Figure 18 *Cross-course vein in Rocks. Note that it is composed solely of quartz and red iron oxide. Broken fragments of an earlier formed quartz vein are embedded in the red iron oxide matrix, indicating that some fault movement has taken place while the vein was being formed.*

the only product from Carclaze open pit. At present day values, over £50 million of tin is estimated to have been produced from Carclaze, which was situated close to the trail from Wheal Martyn to Eden, a few hundred yards northeast of where the trail crosses the A391. Beam and Bunny also yielded tungsten ore (wolframite). Beam was always regarded as a very unhealthy mine to work in and this may be because of the fungal decay of large quantities of timber, gorse, etc which were taken underground in order to staunch the flow of clay slurry into the mine. The workings of Beam underground mine have been seen in Goonbarrow china clay pit **(Figure 17)**, and those of Bunny in Gunheath pit.

As the granite cooled still further, the circulating fluids changed in character; they lost the boron of the early fluids and became even more saline **(Stage 4)**, Even today, some of the salty water is still present in the granite below about 2 km, as deep geothermal boreholes in the Carnmenellis granite have shown. The period of high salinity fluids seems to coincide with the Permian and Triassic Periods, when all of Britain was in the grip of extremely hot and dry conditions,

Figure 19 *Carclaze pit, painted by P. Elliot in 1892. At this time Carclaze's tin producing days were over and china clay from the old pit had yet to become significant. Note the sheep grazing in the pit bottom! The greisen bordered vein swarm which had been the main source of the tin can be seen in the face on the right. The pit was drained by an adit which passed under the hill to discharge at Phernyssick. Reproduced with permission of the Trustees of Wheal Martyn Museum.*

similar to the present day Sahara Desert, and salt pans were developing in Somerset and Cheshire. During this phase the 'cross-course mineralisation' (**Figure 13** – Triassic p. 15 and **Figure 18**, p. 21) were formed, so-called because they usually cut across the older quartz-tourmaline veins at a considerable angle, due to a change in stress direction. They contain no tourmaline, because the fluids no longer contained boron. They are often coloured red by iron oxides and, in places, were rich enough in iron to be worth working for iron ore, as at Restormel Royal Iron mine north of Lostwithiel, iron mines in the Fal Valley and at Coldvreath. This iron must presumably have come from the continued removal of iron from biotite mica by circulating briny fluids.

The zones of kaolinized granite do, at times, seem to follow these cross-course veins and it is possible that there was an early phase of clay mineral formation at this time. However, because of the salinity, it is unlikely to have been kaolinite, more likely to have been illite and/or smectite-type clays.

At the end of the Triassic Period the sea invaded large areas of Britain and the climate became much wetter. Erosion had by now removed most of the cover of rocks on top of the granites. Initially, in the early Jurassic, Cornwall appears to have been submerged beneath the Jurassic sea, but the peninsula seems to have formed a large island through much of the later part of the Jurassic and early part of the Cretaceous Period, when the dinosaurs were the dominant land animals (**Figure 13,** p. 15 – Jurassic - Palaeogene). The climate at this time would have been sub-tropical, rather like present-day Jamaica. After a short submergence beneath the Late Cretaceous sea, warm sub-tropical conditions returned in the Palaeogene.

Deep tropical weathering is known from many locations all over Europe in the Jurassic, Cretaceous and Palaeogene Periods. This tropical weathering is also known as 'chemical weathering', because it has the power to chemically break down many minerals to a kaolinite-rich material. Fresh water from rainfall onto the Cornubian island now entered the system. All the heat from the original intrusion had by now been dissipated (**Stage 5**). However, because of the unusually high contents of radioactive elements, heat derived from the radioactive decay of these elements now took over as the main heat source. This resulted in slow convective circulation of the water through the granite. Periodic earth movements opened up fractures, which further enabled the water to penetrate and circulate through the granite.

It was this constant slow convective circulation of fresh water, driven by radiogenic heat, over a hundred million years or more, which altered the granite to the soft kaolinite-containing material we see today; particularly where the earlier alteration phases had softened up the granite and made it more permeable. Earlier formed smectite and/or illite were also altered to kaolinite and some of the mica as well. During the submergence of the Cornubian island beneath the sea in the early Jurassic and Late Cretaceous salty water entered the granite. The clay minerals responded to this change in the chemistry of the water by slowly changing to minerals such as illite, only to change back to kaolinite once fresh water reinvaded the granite as the island re-emerged from beneath the sea.

Kaolinization seems to have been most active on the downward limbs of the convection cells, where warm surface derived water was being drawn down into the granite. This water probably contained trace amounts of organic compounds derived from the thick tropical vegetation at the surface. It is known that these can accelerate kaolinization.

Deep kaolinization, purely caused by weathering under tropical conditions during the Jurassic and later Periods, is known from many parts of Europe and North America. Deep weathering also probably affected the Cornubian Island and almost certainly contributed to the formation of china clay **(Stage 6).** This weathering continued into the Palaeogene, although this later weathering does not seem to have produced the well-ordered kind of kaolinite which characterises china clay; instead it produced a special kind of disordered kaolinite. Ball clays are characterised by this type of kaolinite and were derived from weathering mantle developed in the Palaeogene. The deeper underground tin and copper mines rarely encountered any kaolinization, except near major cross-courses, emphasising that kaolinization is a surface related process, unlike the metalliferous mineralization, which took place at depth, well away from the surface.

Most of the kaolinite seems to have formed under conditions which are on the borderline between weathering and alteration by circulating hot water (hydrothermal), so it is a rather futile semantic argument to try and decide whether it was formed by weathering or hydrothermal processes. Certainly, there is increasing evidence that the kaolinite repeatedly recrystallized, to give the very pure, highly crystalline form of kaolinite which makes up the bulk of china clay nowadays.

Two generations of kaolinite are usually present in kaolinized granite as illustrated in **Figure 20**:

> **Generation 1**: A 'groundmass' kaolinite, which is typically less than 10-20 microns in diameter. This has been the traditional source of most of the china clay produced.

> **Generation 2**: Large curled stacks of kaolinite up to one tenth of a millimetre in diameter. These appear to have grown in place from solutions moving through the altering granite. There is evidence to

suggest that many of these large stacks may have originated from mica crystals, by kaolinite growing between the layers of the mica crystal. These big stacks can nowadays be recovered from the refining residues by froth flotation and ground to make more product.

Figure 20 *Scanning electron microscope photograph of china clay as it occurs in the ground before processing. Kaolinite is the main mineral forming china clay, mainly occurring as small pseudo-hexagonal plates which can be seen around the periphery. In the centre is a large curled stack of kaolinite and layers forming individual plates can be seen. The picture is about 0.15mm wide.*

The most important areas of kaolinization lie in the western part of the St Austell granite, where the low-iron lithium mica granites provide an ideal parent. However, commercially exploitable deposits also occur in the south-western part of the Dartmoor granite at Lee Moor and on Bodmin Moor. Smaller occurrences have been exploited in the past in most of the other granite masses of South-west England, with the exception of the Isles of Scilly and Lundy.

MINERALS AND ROCKS FOUND IN CHINA CLAY PITS

A great variety of minerals are found in china clay pits, some of which are unusual and rare. Unfortunately, china clay pits can be dangerous places for the uninitiated, so members of the public must not, under any circumstances, visit china clay pits without permission from the china clay company who owns the pit. This includes pits which are currently not in production. The china clay companies, depending on staff availability, usually try to accommodate bona fide parties for educational and scientific visits, and occasional guided tours for tourists are also arranged – enquire at the Museum. Mineral collecting expeditions will always require the participants to be fully equipped with the appropriate safety gear, including hard hat, steel toed boots and high visibility jackets.

Minerals

The following list briefly describes some of the minerals to be found, starting with the commonest and finishing with a few rare and unusual minerals.

Quartz - SiO_2 (Figures 21 and 22) is composed of silica (SiO_2) and is a major constituent of granite. The prominent veins seen in china clay pits are usually partly composed of quartz and the adjoining tips are also composed of quartz **(Figure 23)**. Quartz is a hard mineral, usually pale grey in colour. In some of the veins (particularly cross-course veins), it is possible to find large well-formed six-sided crystals with prismatic terminations. A purple coloured variety of quartz is known as amythyst, often found where a vein contains iron oxides. Fine grained forms of silica, such as chalcedony and opal are sometimes found in china clay pits. The granite boulders (No's 1-5) at the Wheal Martyn Boulder Park show grey quartz crystals to be a major constituent of the granites, as well as the quartz-tourmaline vein (No. 8), which contains some well formed crystals of quartz.

Feldspar - $KAlSi_3O_8$ (Orthoclase), $NaAlSi_3O_8$ (Albite) (Figure 22 and 24) is an aluminium silicate containing alkalis such as sodium, potassium and calcium. It is another major constituent of fresh unaltered granite. Boulders 1-5 at Wheal Martyn show feldspar as the milky white constituent, as opposed to the quartz, which is grey. In china clay pits most of the feldspar has been altered by water passing through the rock to become kaolinite or china clay, as explained in the previous section. Feldspars are creamy-white minerals with a fairly strong cleavage, which means they have a preferred plane of breakage within the crystal, due to the arrangement of atoms within the crystal lattice **(see Figure 31,** p.33). Two kinds of feldspar are commonly found in the local granites: potash feldspar or orthoclase, and soda feldspar or albite (a form of plagioclase). Sometimes, where partial kaolinization has affected the granite, the soda feldspar has been kaolinized, but not the potash and, where large crystals of potash feldspar are present, these can remain intact. They can

Figure 21 *A large individual crystal of quartz, about 7 cm long. Large crystals such as this are only found in veins and pegmatites.*

Figure 22 *Macroscopic photo of Luxulyan granite from Tregarden quarry. The quartz is the grey mineral, the feldspar is white and the shiny black mineral is biotite mica. The width of the photograph covers about 6 mm.*

Figure 23 *Photograph of Dorothy sand tip taken about 30 years ago with a Boyles Buccaneer drilling rig in the foreground. This tip is largely made up of quartz sand.*

Figure 24 *Feldspar crystal (pig's egg) from Wheal Martyn china clay pit. The crystal shows twinning and is about 10 cm long. This is from a partly kaolinised granite where the soda feldspar has kaolinised but the potash feldspar has not, allowing large intact orthoclase feldspar phenocrysts to fall out of the soft matrix.*

Figure 25 *Microscope photomicrograph of biotite mica with minute radioactive inclusions. The radiation from these inclusions has altered the biotite mica around the inclusion, creating the dark coloured spots. Image about 5 mm wide.*

Figure 26 *Sheaves of lithium mica (probably zinnwaldite) from Goonbarrow china clay pit The specimen is about 10 cm long.*

Figure 27 *Haematite from Restormel Royal iron mine, near Lostwithiel, the specimen is about 4 cm long.*

be up to 10 cm long and show the crystal faces and twinning. These are known to the clay workers as 'pigs eggs' or 'pigs ears' **(Figure 24)**. Orthoclase feldspar is a major constituent of pegmatites – see Boulder No. 6 at the Boulder Park. Feldspar is used as a fluxing agent in the manufacture of ceramic articles such as tableware.

Micas - $(K(Mg,Fe)_3(AlSi_3O_{10})(OH)_2$ (Biotite) and $KAl_2(AlSi_3O_{10})(OH)_2$ (Muscovite) (Figure 23 and 25) are the third of the major constituents of granite. The western part of the St Austell granite is unusual in that it contains a great variety of different types of mica. Normally, most granites contain biotite mica; as in the eastern part of the St Austell granite and nearly all of the Bodmin Moor and Land's End granites. Biotite is the dark brown or black flaky mineral in Boulder No. 1 in the Wheal Martyn Boulder Park. Under the microscope biotite from Boulder No. 1 can be seen to contain many tiny inclusions of radioactive minerals **(Figure 25)**; these often have a halo of alteration around them, caused by radiation. The other common mica is muscovite, which is colourless and contains little or no iron. The 'glitter' used for Christmas decorations is sometimes composed of flakes of muscovite. Most normal granites contain both biotite and muscovite. The granites in the western part of the St Austell granite are unusual in containing micas having a significant lithium content (Boulders 4 and 5 at the Wheal Martyn Boulder Park). The commonest lithium-containing mica is zinnwaldite $KLiFe_3+Al(Al,Si_3)O_{10}(F,OH)_2$ **(Figure 26)**, which is usually pale brown. Where the lithium content is high it can become a mauvish mica known as lepidolite $K(Li,Al)_3(Si,Al)_4 O_{10}(F,OH)_2$. Lithium is very much a space-age element; it is used in batteries to power mobile phones, laptops, etc. and for a wide variety of other high-tech uses. If ever fusion power became a reality, it is likely that molten lithium would be the preferred medium for transferring the heat from the reactor to the boilers, so there is a possibility that lithium could become a highly strategic metal.

Tourmaline - Complex aluminium iron silicate with boron. **(Figures 14, 29, 30 and 31)** It has a variable composition and usually occurs as black or dark blue microscopic needles. It is the bluish-black mineral you can see in Boulders 8, 9 and 10 at Wheal Martyn Boulder Park. The black colour of veins seen in Wheal Martyn pit from the Observation Platform is also due to tourmaline. Distinct needles of tourmaline can also be seen in **Figure 29**. Radiating clusters of tourmaline needles are common. The needles appear as somewhat rounded triangles in cross-section, often with striated crystal faces, which enables a distinction to be drawn with biotite mica.

Iron Oxides - Haematite Fe_2O_3 (Figure 27) and Limonite FeO(OH) Iron oxides are similar in composition to rust. In the china clay pits, areas containing too much iron oxide will be stained yellow, brown or red so, as the most important property of china clay is whiteness, these areas have to be avoided or selectively removed. However, in a few places discreet veins of iron oxide, usually in the form of haematite or limonite, can be seen (**Figure 18,** p. 21). Usually these veins are in the cross-course direction (Boulder No. 12 at Wheal Martyn Boulder Park) and, outside the granite, often develop into workable iron ore veins, as at Restormel Royal iron mine, north of Lostwithiel. China clay pits also contain iron nodules, often full of loose fine iron oxide. These were known to china clay workers as 'ink bombs', due to their tendency to split open when hit by the high pressure jet of water from the monitor, resulting in a sudden release of red or brown colour into the clay stream. These iron nodules were probably originally full of iron sulphide (marcasite, FeS_2), which subsequently oxidised to iron oxide.

Turquoise - $CuAl_6(PO_4)_4(OH)_8.5H_2O$ (Figure 28) An unusual and beautifully coloured copper-bearing mineral found in some china clay pits. Unfortunately very little is of gemstone quality. Boulder No 12 at Wheal Martyn has some turquoise. Libethenite $Cu_2PO_4(OH)$ is a closely related green mineral and some occurs in Boulder No 5.

Figure 28 *Turquoise from Gunheath china clay pit, the specimen is 7cm long.*

Topaz – $Al_2SiO_4(OH,F)_2$ A fluorine bearing mineral which is very hard – Hardness 8 on Moh's Scale. Present in several boulders (Nos. 4 and 5) at Wheal Martyn Boulder Park, but difficult to identify, as it is very similar to quartz in appearance. Occurs in veins and in granites, but the best examples are where the granite has been attacked by fluorine bearing solutions and a topaz-bearing 'greisen' produced.

Fluorite – CaF_2 Another fluorine-bearing mineral, usually with a distinctive purple colour (Boulder No. 11 at Wheal Martyn Boulder Park). Occasionally it can be greenish or colourless. Crystals are usually cubic in form. Can occur either in veins (as in Boulder 11), or as crystals scattered through the groundmass of the granite. Occasionally casts of cubic crystals of fluorite can be found, indicating that the original fluorite crystal has been dissolved away by percolating water.

Figure 29 *Macrophotograph of varlamoffite (cream), tourmaline (black needles) and quartz (grey) from Gunheath. Image about 2 cm wide.*

Varlamoffite – $(Sn,Fe)(O,OH)_2$ (Figure 29) An unusual and rare creamy coloured tin mineral which is found in several china clay pits close to Wheal Martyn. The crystal lattice structure is very disordered.

Cassiterite – SnO_2 (Figure 30) is the main commercial ore of tin which has been exploited in Cornwall since Early Bronze Age times. It is a heavy (density 7.0) brown or black mineral, usually occurring in veins or in disseminations

Figure 30 *Cassiterite from Beam mine, now exposed in Goonbarrow china clay pit. The brown mineral is cassiterite, the bluish-black tourmaline and the grey quartz. The cassiterite crystals are unusually coarse - about 0.5 cm across.*

alongside veins. Forms nice prismatic crystals. Can occur in granite or killas, usually worked in an underground mine, or in shallow workings exploiting loose sandy and weathered material in valleys and low lying areas. The latter are known as alluvial deposits and most early tin production was from them.

Wolframite (Fe,Mn)WO$_4$ The ore of tungsten. A shiny black mineral with metallic lustre, which fairly readily alters to a soft brown mineral. It's density is around 7.0, which is similar to that of cassiterite. Before the invention of the magnetic separator around 1900, it was difficult to separate wolframite from cassiterite and the old miners were forced to leave areas containing both ore minerals unworked. Beam mine, in part of the present day Goonbarrow china clay pit is an example of this.

Uranium minerals etc. The uranium minerals, such as pitchblende or uraninite, which were an original component of the granite, are rarely seen, but their alteration products, such as torbernite, can sometimes be found as minute apple-green flakes in china clay pits, especially in areas of relatively weakly kaolinised granite. Small quantities of unusual minerals containing metals such as yttrium, thorium, tantalum, neodymium, etc also occur, particularly in the mica residues. These may merit investigation as sources of these metals in the future.

Rocks

Rocks are composed of a number of minerals, so granite is a rock composed of the minerals quartz, feldspar and mica. Many rocks have already been described, such as granite, elvan, pegmatite, greisen and vein material, so will not be further mentioned in this section. The following are some other interesting rocks to be found in china clay country:

China stone is a trade term used to describe a kind of hard pale coloured granite almost free of kaolinization, which is also unusually low in dark coloured minerals and hence has an exceptionally low iron content. It is a mixture of quartz, feldspar and colourless mica, together with small amounts of topaz and fluorite. When ground up it can be used by potters in a ceramic body, together with other ingredients such as china clay, ground flint and ball clay to make high quality ceramics. Its light colour and easy workability also make it suitable as a building stone, when it is known as 'St Stephen's Stone'. The main occurrence of this type of stone is between St Stephen and St Dennis (Boulder No. 2 at Wheal Martyn).

Luxullianite is a special kind of altered granite, which is composed of black tourmaline, with pink feldspar **(Figure 31)**, probably produced by boron-rich fluids altering a coarse grained granite. A large block is in the main Museum at Wheal Martyn. Originally found near Luxulyan and much prized by the Victorians for

Figure 31 *Luxullianite from Tregarden quarry, Luxulyan. The feldspar is pink and the bluish-black mineral is tourmaline. The prominent lines in the feldspar crystals are cleavage planes, which follow the crystal lattice structure. Specimen 10 cm wide.*

ornamental use. Polished slabs are very striking. The sarcophagus of the Duke of Wellington in the crypt of St Paul's Cathedral in London has been carved from a block of this stone.

Porphyry is a rather old fashioned term for rocks of granitic composition containing large crystals of feldspar and quartz set in a finer grained matrix. Many so-called 'porphyries' are really either elvans or fine grained granites. Sometimes porphyries make good ornamental stones and can be polished to make tiles and facing slabs, e.g. the Tremore Porphyry from near Lanivet.

Schorl is a rather loose term, sometimes applied to a dark bluish-black variety of tourmaline, but locally very often applied to a rock composed mainly of tourmaline and quartz when, strictly speaking, it should be called 'schorl-rock'.

Killas is a wonderfully useful 'sack' term for the granite geologist to use, as it describes the 'country rocks' into which the granite mass has been intruded. Killas are usually the Devonian slates, sandstones and igneous rocks surrounding the granite, but adjacent to the granite they will have been altered by the heat and mineralising-fluids from the granite. This zone of altered rocks around the granite is known as the 'metamorphic aureole'. Where boron rich solutions emanating from the granite have altered the killas, they can produce a striking rock with the original sedimentary laminations picked out as black and white stripes, usually crumpled and folded.

Greenstone is a term used for basic lavas, minor intrusions, etc. formed at, or soon after, the time when Devonian and Carboniferous sediments were being laid down. Most of these volcanic rocks were of a different composition to granite, containing more iron and magnesium and less silica, resulting in minerals such as pyroxene and amphibole which are usually dark green in colour, hence the term. Confusingly, these rocks are often called 'blue elvan' in Cornwall.

LOCATING AND EVALUATING CHINA CLAY DEPOSITS

Today, the locations of most china clay deposits in the western part of the St Austell granite are well established. However, as recently as fifty years ago, the location of the deposits were imprecisely known, except adjacent to the working pits. In those days the development of the pit largely depended on the Captain's instinct for where the clay lay. Systematic pitting had been employed in the early part of the twentieth century to locate kaolinised areas, but these hand-dug pits could only rarely establish the full depth of the deposits. Photographs taken by Joseph Coon, a well known local geologist, directing this sort of exploration work on Bodmin Moor have been found. These photographs date back to 1910.

When simple geophysical equipment became available after the Second World War, it began to be employed by the china clay industry. The chosen technique was resistivity, which entailed applying an electrical current into the ground and then measuring the potential drop between two other electrodes placed in line between the current electrodes (the Wenner electrode configuration). By traversing across the terrain with a constant electrode separation (usually 100 feet), a picture of the variation in subsurface resistance could be obtained and contour maps of ground resistivity built up. Kaolinized granite has a much higher water content than fresh unkaolinized granite, so has a lower resistivity, so low resistance areas tended to contain clay and high resistance areas were usually indicative of solid unaltered granite. The technique was rapid and inexpensive; the author has vivid memories from the 1960s of covering vast areas of ECC's mineral interest in this way, with teams of works apprentices and students moving the electrodes for each reading. The technique was useful in finding areas where there was little china clay, as tips could then be planned for these locations. Low resistance did not always mean china clay, as wet boggy areas tended to give a low resistance signature, irrespective of whether there was clay or unaltered granite below the bog. Also, resistivity surveying could not give any information about the quality of the clay. Gravity geophysics, which measures the density of the rocks below the surface was also tried. Kaolinised areas have a lower density than unkaolinised granite.

To test for quality and find out the true depth of the china clay deposits it was necessary to drill boreholes and recover samples which could be tested in the laboratory. Kaolinized granite is a very difficult medium to drill, as the combination of the soft kaolinised granite, which all too readily disperses into a slurry, and the very hard near vertical quartz-tourmaline veins, is a real challenge to the driller. To begin with, the drillers were only able to recover slurry samples, but it was found these could be misleading, due to soft kaolinized granite caving into the hole. Special coring techniques were then developed in the 1960-1970 period, which depended on the use of drilling rigs with high torque and slow rotation speeds and special face-discharge core barrels **(Figure 23,** p. 27**)** These were able to produce reliable cores which could be tested in the laboratory. Twenty or more different properties would be measured, covering both ceramic and paper applications. Many thousands of boreholes have now been drilled, so the location and quality of the china clay deposits is now reasonably well known. More recently, mathematical processing techniques have been developed to enable the drill results to be incorporated into pit development planning, which can also be integrated into market planning.

CHINA CLAY AND THE ENVIRONMENT

The environmental impact of the china clay industry has been a matter of debate for many years. Around 170 million tonnes have been produced to date, so with a waste to clay ratio of 9 : 1, this means that around one and a half billion tonnes of material have been moved. This massive displacement of material has turned a rather bleak and uninteresting piece of moorland and poor quality farmland into a dramatic landscape of waste tips, open pits, some disused and flooded, residue (mica) lagoons, haulways, processing sites and settlements **(Frontispiece, & Figure 32)**, which has provided inspiration to artists, writers and poets **(Figure 19,** p.22**)**.

Comparison between china clay working and other mineral deposits

The waste produced for every tonne of china clay produced, is made up of 4.5 tonnes of rock, 3.5 tonnes of sand and one tonne of fine mica-rich material (For details of china clay mining and processing see: Thurlow, C. 2005 China Clay from Cornwall and Devon, Cornish Hillside Publications.). Some of the sand and rock waste is sold for construction purposes locally, such as concrete block making, roadstone and concreting aggregate, but far more is produced than can be consumed. The excess waste sand, rock (stent) and overburden forms large tips which are conspicuous. There are, in addition, mica lagoons which take the silty-sand residue produced by the refining of the clay, a substantial component of which is mica.

Figure 32 *General view of Gunheath pit looking north, the deep pit can be seen, as well as several old tips.*

One of the most frequently asked questions is: 'Why can't the waste be put back into the china clay pits?' To answer this we must make a comparison between china clay working and other types of mineral working **(Figure 33)**.

'Massive' type of mineral deposit, e.g. china clay **(Figure 33, Top)**. A typical china clay deposit is funnel shaped and was formed by surface-derived water being drawn down into the granite on the downward limb of a hydrothermal convection cell. The maximum slope on the side of a china clay pit is governed by the engineering properties of the rocks making up the slope; it is rarely possible to make it steeper than the angle shown in the diagram (35°). The main future reserves can be seen in the diagram to lie under the deeper part of the pit and the best quality is often found overlying the stem of the funnel. Backfilling of any part of the pit will clearly result in some of the china clay reserve being made impossible to work. Note that the large tonnage of china clay on the left hand side of the pit is unavailable for future working because of the presence of a public road and a village. The main point to emphasise is that with this type of deposit it is usually impossible to start backfilling until one is sure that all the exploitable ore has been removed, otherwise resources which might have been worked by future generations will be sterilised and wasted, which goes to the heart of what true 'sustainability' is all about. Indeed, one needs also to ask whether backfilling should commence while the unexploited china clay on the left is still there; for future generations may think it is acceptable to move the road and settlement. Should we waste resources like this?

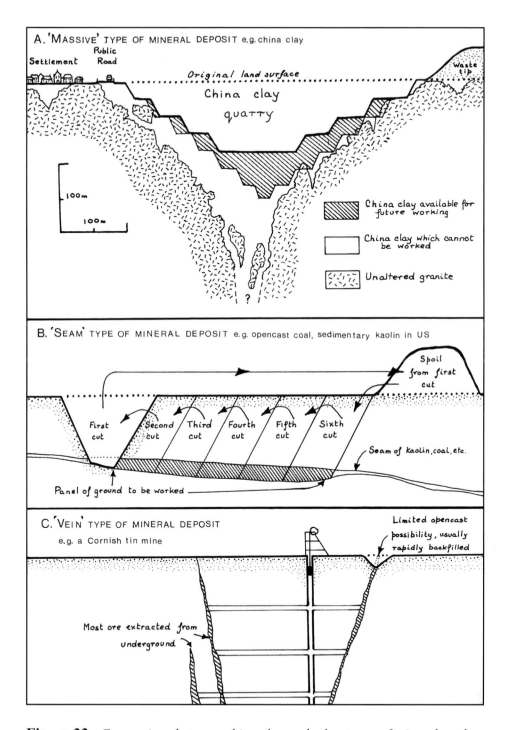

Figure 33 *Comparison between china clay and other types of mineral working, see text for details.*

'**Seam' (Figure 33, Middle)** type of mineral deposit, e.g. opencast coal, ball clay or sedimentary kaolin. In this type of operation the material to be worked occurs as a near horizontal or gently dipping 'bed'. If it is not too deep, it can be 'strip-mined' by digging a deep trench down to the seam ('first cut' on the left hand side of the diagram) and placing the excavated material at the far end of the panel of ground to be worked. Successive cuts can then be made, with the waste in each case being cast into the adjacent worked out cut. Typically a machine called a dragline can dig and dump the excavated material all in one movement. Finally the original pile of waste can be cast back into the final cut. With this method of mining, re-instatement can start as soon as the initial cut has been backfilled. Only the cut where actual mining is in progress need be open at any one time.

In developed countries, such as Britain and the US, very high standards for restoring strip mines are now required by law and the ground will be left after mining in as good a state (sometimes better) than before mining started, but in some developing countries (and in the past in some developed countries) the effects of unregulated strip mining can result in an unsightly wasteland.

'**Vein' (Figure 33, Bottom)** type of mineral deposit, e.g. Cornish tin mine. Underground mining is much more costly than open-pit mining. Where the commodity being extracted is of high value, such as a non-ferrous metal, and where it occurs in narrow steeply dipping veins extending down to a considerable depth, then underground mining will probably be the only option, apart from some very limited opencast working near the surface. Cornish tin mining is a classic example of this type of mining. Sometimes a 'seam' is worked at depth, as with an underground coal mine, but this usually means that the seam can only be partially excavated, because of the need to leave support.

The problem of what to do with china clay waste

Until recently it has been impossible to transport china clay waste to major conurbations outside Cornwall, because the cost of transport would have been several times greater than the price the waste could command as a building material in a location such as the Home Counties. However, with the introduction of the Primary Aggregate Tax in April 2002, markets for china clay waste outside Cornwall are beginning to develop. A simple calculation shows that transport of all waste out of Cornwall by road or rail is out of the question. To move current annual waste production would mean a 40t lorry leaving the county every minute, 24 hours a day, every day of the year; by rail it would mean forty 2000t trains a day. Would this be environmentally acceptable? Transport by sea is clearly another option. However, it would be unrealistic to assume that more than a fraction of the total waste generated every year could be moved out of the county, so there is still a requirement for tipping space, subject to planning permissions.

In recent years much progress has been made in softening the impact of the workings by revegetating the tips and residue dams. Concurrently concerns are being raised about the future of some historic buildings and sites concerned with the early history of the industry. The setting up of Wheal Martyn Museum with support from the china clay industry and other bodies **(Figure 34)**, now known officially as 'The China Clay Country Park, Mining and Heritage Centre', as well as the formation of a China Clay History Society is a reflection of interest in the historical development of the industry, by local people and visitors.

Most waste tips naturally revegetate very slowly, especially if they are composed solely of sand and rock, with no moisture retaining material mixed in, such as micaceous residue or overburden. Depending on the situation of the tip and without any artificial intervention, it will remain barren for about 30 years before ling and heather begin to take hold. In a further ten years small shrubs appear, followed around ten years later by plants such as sallow (a form of dwarf willow) and rhododendron. A hundred years can pass before the tip becomes fully colonised by trees. China clay waste materials are deficient in nutrients, particularly nitrogen, making growth difficult to sustain. On steep sided tips the surface is very free draining and susceptible to erosion, making nutrient retention difficult. On the flat-topped mica lagoons, erosion is less of a problem, but some plant nutrients are absent.

Experiments and large-scale field trials on various kinds of china clay waste have enabled methods to be developed, using appropriate plants, which allow revegetation to be rapidly and successfully achieved. A disused mica

Figure 34 *Wheal Martyn Museum at Carthew showing the Main Entrance.*

Figure 35 *Maggie Pies mica dam during experimental trials to find out which plants would grow well on a substrate of mica residue. In the foreground, on the right, are clumps of lupins which are helpful in fixing nitrogen in a free draining substrate such as this face of Kernick mica dam. Another pioneer species, sallow (a kind of shrubby willow), can be seen further down the slope.*

lagoon site (Maggie Pies) was used for a series of large scale trials **(Figure 35)**. Experimental plots were laid out, with a range of grasses, legumes and shrubs, each plot being given different fertiliser and aftercare treatments. This resulted in the selection of special blends of grass seed, together with nitrogen-fixing legumes such as clover and lupin. These accelerate the rate of nutrient build-up and enables the sward to become established and ready for tree planting.

The balance and management of plant types is crucial and the after care needed to ensure a sustainable plant cover is achieved continues for ten years or more. Trees can succeed where shelter and nutrients are available, as was shown in experimental plantings on Littlejohns sand tip. Here short-term trees such as pine and alder were used to provide initial shelter and nutrient, giving way to long-lived native species such as oak.

There are some access problems to the steep slopes of tips. For such situations a hydroseeding technique has been developed in which a slurry of fertiliser and mulch with seed suspended in it is sprayed from a specially built vehicle. The mulch protects the seed from the effects of adverse climatic changes and reduces losses due to erosion.

Traditional agricultural methods are used to develop pasture land on mica lagoons, on back-filled pits and on re-shaped tips. These areas benefit greatly from being grazed. In the early 1970s St Kilda Soay sheep were introduced to these new pastures. Being light, agile and independent they are well situated to improve the condition of the pasture, putting land to commercial use at an early stage. Areas that are inappropriate for agricultural after-use are frequently planted as woodland.

In locations where plant life of special significance has been disturbed or where particular amenity use is envisaged, the spread of natural vegetation is encouraged by the transportation of seed. The two methods most commonly used are the removal to a new site of large cut clumps of the soil containing seeds and plant matter, or by flailing. Flailing involves the collection of seed-bearing branches and shoots from heathers and similar plants, which are cut and mixed with a mulch for spreading onto the new surface. Also used are translocation of seed-rich soils, and seed collection (non-destructive) and sowing. The resulting plant life is appropriate for the newly created habitat and provides a food source for insects and these in turn attract the small rodents which attract birds and other predators. In this way the land reclamation provides a basis for the return of a full and balanced ecosystem appropriate to the site.

In recent years, waste piles have changed considerably in shape and design. The old familiar conical tips produced by a skip running up an incline to tip at the top **(Figures 23,** p. 27 **& 32,** p.36**)** were satisfactory as long as the rate of tipping was modest and the tips were not allowed to become too large. However, following the Aberfan tragedy, it became apparent that the larger tips would have to be designed as carefully engineered structures, so flat topped tips emplaced by dumpers and/or conveyors became the norm. The next step was to smooth the angular outline of the tips, so they became more like natural hills and could blend in with the landscape. The major clay company Imerys is now working in partnership with English Nature to create hundreds of hectares of lowland heath on former china clay waste tips.

China clay country as an amenity

The natural history of the workings are creating much interest, both in terms of their biology and the geology. As described above, a large area of china clay country is now well on the way to becoming natural heath and woodland, although the spread of rhododendron scrub is proving to be serious problem requiring robust management, as well as other invasive plants such as Japanese knotweed. In addition to the managed restoration areas, there are valleys and areas between the pits and tips which have naturally revegetated which, together with the flooded pits and their steep sides, are creating an area of quite exceptional biodiversity. Many of the natural habitats created by china clay working are unusual, so they tend to be colonised by rare plants, some very rare indeed, such as certain mosses. Consequently, as investigations proceed into these habitats, a number of Sites of Special Scientific Interest are being designated.

The working pits also provide a wonderful window into the local geology, which has attracted researchers from all over the world. With the benefit of these magnificent exposures, research scientists have been able to deduce many important processes concerned with the formation of mineral deposits such as tin/copper and china clay. Many important scientific papers and concepts have been based on field work and samples from the china clay pits. Indeed the section on the geology of these deposits in the early part of this booklet could not have been written without the benefit of all this research work. Going hand-in-hand with this research work is the educational value for geology and mining students, who are able to visit the pits and see features which otherwise they might have to travel to the other side of the world to see **(Figure 36)**.

Figure 36 *Party of students from Camborne School of Mines being instructed by the author in Goonbarrow china clay pit in the early 1990s. Many of these students will have gone on to hold responsible positions in mining industries and environmental organisations all over the world. (Photo: Dr Robin Shail).*

More recently a whole series of high quality trails have been opened up in china clay country for walkers, cyclists and horse riders to use and these already show promise to be a major amenity for visitors and local people alike, from Bugle to the Eden Project, from there to Wheal Martyn, from Par Beach to St Blazey and in the area around Blackpool pit. Altogether over 20 miles of tracks between Bodmin and Mevagissey are now open, the trails are mostly off road and are well surfaced. Most are connected to rail and bus stations. For details of these trails, enquire at the Wheal Martyn Museum shop.

Disused pits will also become useful water resevoirs, offsetting the need for building more upland resevoirs by water supply companies.

KAOLIN (CHINA CLAY) IN THE REST OF THE WORLD

Deposits of kaolinitic clay are known throughout the world as 'kaolin' deposits; 'china clay' is a term used only in Britain for kaolin deposits. World kaolin production is over 20 million tonnes; the largest producing nations are the USA, Brazil and the UK, who together produce over half of all world production. The high value kaolins used in paper and in better quality ceramics are internationally traded and there is intense competition between the main producers. The kaolins used for paper coating form the largest and most valuable market and this type of kaolin is costly enough to justify shipment half way around the world, so the logistics of sea transport in bulk carriers becomes an important factor.

The more significant producers of kaolin in 2003 were:

USA	8,010,000	tonnes
Brazil	2,300,000	"
UK	2,097,000	"
P.R. China	1,600,000	"
Korea (South)	1,100,000	"
Germany	738,000	"
Czech Republic	582,000	"
Spain	450,000	"
France	323,000	"
Australia	280,000	"

Significant tonnages of kaolin were also produced in India, Ukraine, Indonesia, New Zealand, Malaysia, South Africa, Portugal and Venezuela.

Source: British Geological Survey

Whilst the U.K. was a major exporter of high value kaolins to North America in the early part of the 20th century, since the Second World War paper coating kaolins from the large sedimentary deposits in Georgia and South Carolina have entered the European market place. Rapid development of large kaolin deposits in the Amazon Basin in Brazil in recent years has now resulted in Brazil becoming the second largest producer in the world, with its kaolin also competing strongly in Europe. Taken together with the competition coming from ultra-fine ground carbonates made from marble and chalk, also used for filling and coating by the paper and other industries, the future for china clay from SW England is sure to be competitive.

Climate has an important influence on the feasibility of kaolin production. In Central Europe, where long periods of freezing conditions in the winter are normal, the whole plant and all pipework has to be enclosed and heated, to enable production to continue through the winter. The Cornish style of working simply could not function under these conditions. Conversely, in hot dry conditions, the lack of water may be an insuperable barrier to kaolin processing. In any case, the water for kaolin processing needs to be chemically purer than that used in many arid countries for human consumption. In remote areas the lack of a local market may inhibit the building of a small or medium sized plant, but a really large plant may be able to successfully trade internationally, particularly if large ships are able to load close at hand.

Because of all these factors, a geologist working internationally on the evaluation of kaolin deposits must understand in detail not only how the kaolin can be processed and upgraded, but also the way in which kaolins are used in the consuming industries and the economics of moving the kaolin to the customer. Defining the reserves of china clay, especially for a new deposit overseas, involves understanding all these factors. As a result 'real' geology may only occupy a minor part of an industrial geologists time.

Types of kaolin deposit

Kaolin deposits may be broadly classified into:

Primary - Kaolin deposits formed in situ by the alteration of existing rocks containing aluminium silicates such as feldspars, micas, etc. The alteration process may take place at depth under hydrothermal conditions or near the surface as a result of chemical weathering in response to a humid tropical or sub-tropical climate. Alteration by hot volcanic gases and springs (solfatara) can also produce a special type of primary kaolin deposit.

Secondary - Kaolin deposits formed by sedimentation, usually under fresh-water conditions. These include sedimentary kaolins proper, kaolinitic sands and ball clays.

Ball clays are sedimentary clays characterised by a particularly favourable combination of high strength, plasticity and fired brightness, which makes them especially suitable for ceramics. Lithification of ball clay-like clays can produce fireclays and flint clays.

Unfortunately this apparently simple classification is often not applicable in practice, because many deposits have been formed by multi-stage processes. A bed of clay may be laid down as part of a sedimentary sequence and then its clay mineralogy may be profoundly changed by later weathering or as a response to changing physico-chemical conditions after the sediment has been laid down. In the case of the china clay deposits of Southwest England, it has been found that both high and low temperature hydrothermal phases are required to explain the formation of the deposits, and the low temperature hydrothermal processes are difficult to distinguish from the effects of deep weathering.

Kaolin in Europe

The largest kaolin producer in Europe is Britain, the Czech Republic and Germany produce just over half a million tonnes a year and smaller quantities are produced in Spain, France and Portugal. Over the last thirty years or so many of smaller kaolin operations in Europe have closed, either because they have become uncompetitive because of their small size, or because they exhausted their reserves. Consequently overall kaolin production in Europe has tended to decline.

If we ignore political boundaries, then the kaolin deposits of Europe may be conveniently grouped as follows:

(a) Southwest England - china clay and ball clay, already dealt with.
(b) Central Europe - Bavaria and Bohemia, many different types of deposit.
(c) Ukraine - Mesozoic weathering of ancient granitic rocks.
(d) France - kaolinization of the granitic rocks in ancient massifs.
(e) Iberia - mainly kaolinitic sands.

Central Europe - Bavaria and Bohemia

The fact that kaolin production in central Europe comes from three different countries tends to conceal the fact that the area which contains the majority of these deposits is relatively compact. However, there is a great variety of different types of deposit within this area giving rise to a large number of small to medium sized operations. Weathering has had a dominant influence in the generation of the kaolin deposits. This region contains the oldest kaolin operations in Europe (if we exclude ball clays), and the Aue and Colditz kaolins were exploited for porcelain production several decades before Cookworthy started his china clay operations in Cornwall.

The kaolinised Bunter arkoses of the Hirschau-Schnaittenbach area of Bavaria yield good quality kaolins which are mainly used for filler and ceramics. The parent material is a kaolinized sandstone of Triassic age. The yield of kaolin from the Bavarian kaolins is quite low, at around 10-15%, the remaining material is mainly quartz sand, much of which is sold for constructional or industrial purposes. The excess sand that cannot be sold forms large sand tips which have been developed into a resort area with skiing on the sides of one of the tips of fine sand.

The kaolinised Permian volcanics to the north of the Erzgebirge in the old DDR are of considerable geological interest. Colditz castle sits on a volcanic edifice belonging to this period of volcanicity and one of the earliest kaolin operations anywhere in Europe was nearby. Weathering in the Tertiary has caused a volcanic flow rather like the elvans of Cornwall to be altered to a mixture of kaolinite and a mixed layer smectite/illite clay mineral which has excellent ceramic properties. The principal pits are at Groppendorf, Frieden and Gluckauf, in the Kemmlitz area **(Figure 37)**.

Figure 37 *Kaolinized porphyry (a kind of volcanic flow) in Groppendorf pit, Kemmlitz, in the eastern part of Germany. This is a valuable clay for ceramic purposes. It is being worked by means of a bucket ladder excavating system, hence the very regular faces. Such a working system would not work in china clay because of the hard quartz veins.*

The kaolinitic sands of the Plzen area (Czech Republic) are of late Carboniferous age and contain a mixture of kaolinite laid down at the time of deposition and kaolinite formed later. A wide range of kaolins can be produced from the main operations at Kasnejov and Horni Briza, including paper filling and coating clays and ceramic clays. The kaolinised granites of Karlovy Vary are more like the china clay deposits of Cornwall and Devon; although the Czech geologists have always maintained that weathering is the principle cause of the kaolinization. The similarity with SW England centres around the granites, which are highly evolved Variscan granites, with much evidence of greisening and tourmalinization and some Sn/W mineralization. Some of the clays from this area are highly valued for ceramic production.

Ukraine - Mesozoic weathering

The principal kaolin deposits of the Ukraine are at Prosianaya and Glukhovetsk. Combined production from these two centres has been as high as 1 million tonnes a year, nearly all of which was consumed within the former eastern bloc; very little has been exported.

Figure 38 *A large bucket-wheel excavator at Prosianaya in the Ukraine working granite which has been kaolinized by deep weathering during the Jurassic and Cretaceous Periods.*

Throughout the Ukrainian shield deep Mesozoic chemical weathering of the Pre-Cambrian rocks is widespread. This kind of deep weathering is also widespread in continental Europe. The Prosianaya **(Figure 38)** and Glukhovetsk kaolin deposits have been formed by the alteration of Pre-Cambrian granites and gneisses poor in dark minerals. Both deposits are capable of yielding paper filling and coating kaolins. There are many other kaolin deposits in the Ukraine and southern Urals.

France - The ancient massifs

Granitic rocks make up a substantial part of the ancient massifs of Brittany and the Massif Central. Some are equivalent in age to the Variscan granites of SW England and some are much older. A large number of occurrences of kaolinization are known in both massifs, but most are on a much smaller scale than those of Cornwall. Over the years many kaolin workings have been attempted and currently there are four operations in operation in Brittany and one in the Massif Central.

Thirty years ago there were three kaolin operations clustered in and around the Echassieres granite in the Massif Central, but there is only one now left in production - Kaolins de Beauvoir. The Echassieres granite is tiny - less than 1 km in diameter - but it contains many of the characteristic features of the St Austell granite on a small scale; the granite is lithium rich and has associated Sn/W mineralization.

Two of the kaolin operations in Brittany are on the south coast at Ploemeur near Lorient and are working kaolinized granitic rocks. One of the other operations - Kaolins du Finistere at Berrien - is nearer the north coast, south of Morlaix and the fourth operation is near St Brieuc and involves a kaolinized carbonaceous granite, although where the carbon in the granite has come from remains a mystery.

Iberia

Between the headwaters of the River Tagus and Valencia there are extensive deposits of kaolinitic sands in the Lower Cretaceous. They probably represent arkosic sands which were subsequently kaolinized by circulating groundwater. The quality of the kaolin is sufficient for paper filling and coating applications, as well as for ceramics; however, the yield of kaolin is low and the sale of industrial sand is a necessary feature of many of the operations.

Portugal's kaolin industry is partly centred on kaolinitic sands north of Lisbon, and partly based on primary deposits in the north around Oporto and extending further northwards into NW Spain (Galicia). These latter deposits have much in common with those in Brittany and weathering has probably played an important part in their genesis.

Kaolin outside Europe

The most important deposits of kaolin outside Europe are in Georgia, USA and the Amazon Basin, Brazil. Currently Georgia and South Carolina in the United States produce about 8 million tonnes of refined kaolin a year and the Amazon Basin produces just over 2 million tonnes a year, nearly all for export. Both countries exploit sedimentary kaolins.

Georgia and South Carolina

This is the largest kaolin producing area in the world and has been since the outbreak of the Second World War. The sedimentary kaolins of Georgia and South Carolina are contained in sediments of Late Cretaceous and Early Tertiary age which were deposited in a coastal or tidal flat environment. The sedimentary material originated from deep chemical weathering mantle developed under tropical conditions on the ancient rocks of the Piedmont (tropical chemical weathering is explained below in the section on the Amazon Basin).

This soft weathered material was then eroded and transported to the coastal plain, where the clay and sand settled out in lagoons, oxbow lakes, etc. **(Figure 39)**. High titania contents of most of the clays suggest that they were laid down as 'common clays' with a relatively high iron and titania content. The iron content was then greatly reduced by prolonged leaching associated with tropical weathering. The occurrence of large vermicular growths of kaolinite confirms that considerable changes in the clay mineralogy have taken place after deposition of the sediment. The chemical weathering was so severe that in places it broke down the kaolinite and removed it's silica, thereby creating bauxite minerals (hydrated aluminium oxides). Sometimes the bauxites were resilicated back to kaolinite.

The older Late Cretaceous kaolins tend to be whiter and coarser grained, whilst the Early Tertiary kaolins are finer grained and slightly grey. Most of the best white kaolins have been worked out and the kaolins being worked nowadays require many stages of beneficiation to make them commercially acceptable. The industry tends to be organised in a rather different way to Cornwall, with large centralised processing plants fed by pipeline or truck from a whole series of strip mines which are essentially short lived in nature. A high proportion of the clay brought to the processing plant can be made into saleable product, so there is nowhere near the same waste disposal problem as in Cornwall. In many cases the excavated clay is degritted at the mine site before being sent by pipeline to the central processing plant. In this way the unnecessary transport of unwanted material is minimized.

Figure 39 *Sedimentary kaolin, near Sandersville, Georgia showing striking sedimentary structures, probably produced by an oxbow meander being filled with sand and clay during the Late Cretaceous. Subsequent intense chemical weathering has converted the clay to the valuable white kaolin being worked in the foreground. The trees are about 10m high.*

The sedimentary kaolins are worked as strip mines (see description of a strip mine on Pages 36 & 37) and high standards of re-instatement are achieved. Restored areas are often planted with trees for pulpwood. Most of the kaolin is used internally in North America, but some is exported through the coastal ports of Georgia and South Carolina, such as Savannah. Some of the kaolin is flash calcined (briefly heated to a high temperature) to make special products for paper, paint and plastics, where high opacity is required. Other kaolins are chemically treated to make zeolites.

The kaolin operations are centred around the towns of Sandersville and Augusta, which are real 'southern bible belt' towns. Practically everyone in Sandersville is connected in some way with the kaolin industry. The sound of the freight trains taking away the kaolin to all parts of North America is one of the most evocative features of Sandersville, which announces at the city limit that it is the 'City of Kaolin'. English China Clays built up their largest overseas operation in Sandersville; it now belongs to Imerys.

The Amazon Basin

Tropical weathering in and around the Amazon Basin has created ideal conditions for the widespread development of deep lateritic (chemical) weathering profiles.

A typical chemical (or lateritic) weathering profile is shown in Figure 40, and shows the typical sequence of zones which characterise this type of profile. Incidentally, it is the total absence of this type of zonation in the china clay deposits of SW England which indicates that tropical weathering cannot be the main cause of the kaolinization.

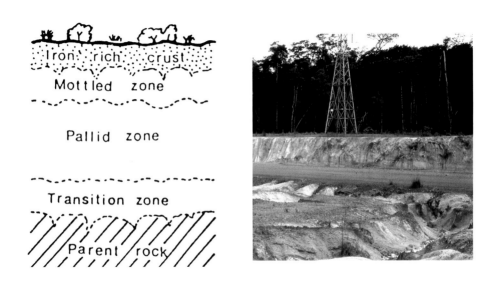

Figure 40 Left: *An idealised chemical weathering profile, as developed in humid tropical environments.*
Right: *The pallid zone of a typical tropical weathering profiile in Surinam, South America, note the intensive iron staining. Bauxites are worked nearby.*

Throughout the tropics there are immense quantities of tropical weathering mantle. The pallid zone **(Figure 40)** is often the thickest zone in the profile and is characterised by kaolinite being the dominant clay mineral. Most pallid zone material contains a great deal of iron oxide as well, which colours the clayey material red, brown, pink or yellow. Only under exceptional conditions, notably when the parent rock is very low in iron, or where the weathering conditions have been particularly prolonged or intense, will the pallid zone be wholly white.

However, if the pallid zone material is eroded and transported away to a sedimentary basin it can, under the right circumstances, lose a great deal of its iron, so the clay which is laid down in the basin is much lower in iron than the parent weathered material. The ball clays in the fault-formed sedimentary basins of Devon show this, as they have a much lower iron content than their parent weathered material.

The clays laid down in the sedimentary basin may be subjected to further chemical weathering, leading to the leaching away of more iron. This seems to have been an important mechanism in the formation of the Georgia/South Carolina kaolins.

Intense chemical weathering under tropical conditions can lead to a further weathering stage, where the silica in the kaolinite is stripped out and transported away in solution. This leaves hydrated aluminium oxide, or bauxite – the ore of aluminium. Some commercial bauxite deposits are underlain by a pallid zone which can be worked as a source of kaolin.

The Amazon kaolins. In the central part of the Amazon Basin there is a huge quantity of kaolin bearing sediment which, in places, is capable of being processed to make commercial kaolins. The first operation to exploit these clays was created by the American shipping magnate Daniel K. Ludwig as part of grand plan to develop the hinterland around the Rio Jari, on the north side of the basin. In this area the hills are capped by bauxitic clay and this is underlain by a thick sequence of very fine grained kaolinitic clay up to 30m thick of Pliocene age (Late Tertiary), **(Figure 41)**. This has been exploited in a large open pit by the Rio Jari, which feeds a processing plant on the opposite bank. One of the keys to the success of this operation is the fact that the product can be loaded directly into 45,000 tonne bulk carriers right beside the plant, which can then take the clay directly to Europe, North America or Japan.

The success of the Jari operation encouraged many large international mining houses to look elsewhere in the Amazon Basin, which resulted in the finding of large high quality sedimentary kaolin deposits up the Rio Capim on the south side of the Amazon Basin. The Rio Capim is characterised by shallows and has many sand banks, so is not navigable to large vessels. Consequently a 150 km pipeline was constructed to take the clay to a plant near Belem, where the kaolin is processed and loaded onto ocean going vessels. Over the last 15 years the output from the Capim plants has increased rapidly and is now in excess of one million tonnes a year, with Imerys one of the producers. Resources of high quality kaolin in this area are very large. As European kaolin output declines, it is the Amazon Basin which is taking over and providing for the growth in world consumption of kaolin. However, as strip mining is involved, the destruction of Amazonian rain forest is a factor that should not be overlooked.

Figure 41 *Massive kaolin deposit, Rio Jari, Amazon Basin. Brazil is now the second largest kaolin producer in the world, mainly due to recent development of the extensive deposits in the catchments of the Rio Jari and Rio Capim tributaries of the Amazon river system. Rio Jari in the background.*

Peoples Republic of China

Figure 42 *Two early views of 1979 showing the Suzhou kaolin mine in China.*
Left: *The shaft head at the mine. The author is the tallest of the group wearing basketry safety hats!*
Right: *Kaolin piles drying alongside the processing plant.*

A great variety of kaolin deposits are exploited in China, where the earliest kaolin workings for porcelain manufacture were situated. The original clay mine at Kauling has long been abandoned. A large underground mine near Suzhou **(Figure 42)** exploits kaolinized sills of granitic composition. The clay contains halloysite as well as kaolinite. Rapid development of kaolin production in China has resulted in a number of other operations being opened, notably at Maoming, Guangdong Province. Most of the kaolin produced in China is absorbed by the rapidly growing internal market.

Australasia

The major bauxite deposits at Weipa in Northern Queensland are underlain by a pallid zone which contains much kaolinite. This has been exploited in a plant built near the bauxite operation.

Weathered granites at Pittong near Ballarat are exploited for kaolin which is processed for use in the Australian market.

Altered rhyolitic volcanics in the North Island of New Zealand, near Whangarei yield clays largely composed of halloysite, which are exported for use in high quality ceramics.

THE FUTURE?

A question very often asked is 'how long will the resources of china clay in Cornwall and Devon last?' This is an almost impossible question to answer, as the price that china clay will fetch in the future will govern how much can be profitably worked. Factors such as the competition, the waste to clay ratio as pits get deeper, taxation and environmental restraints will all influence future viability and hence how much china clay will eventually be won from the deposits in SW England.

During the last 45 years in which I have been concerned with the industry, I have seen the pre-eminent position of china clay from SW England gradually eroded, with the development of large export-capable operations, first in Georgia, USA and then in other locations such as the Amazon Basin and the Czech Republic. Many small operations in Europe have closed, so there has been an overall reduction in the output of kaolin from Europe. In recent years this reduction has been balanced by the expansion of production in the Amazon Basin, although whether this is an environmental gain, because of the consequent destruction of Amazonian rain forest, may be a debateable point.

The life of the industry will be considerably extended if china clay which is sterilised at present, because of existing roads and settlements, can be worked, but whether society will accept the sort of changes this would involve in the future is something only time will tell.

It is tempting to think that we shall see the huge waste piles in the St Austell area being reworked in the late 21st century as a source of building material. Clay works sand is especially useful for beach make-up operations as it is coarse and angular and therefore does not get washed off the beach like normal fine sand would. If serious sea level rise sets in as a result of global warming, this could become a major market.

An even more speculative possibility is that the rare and unusual minerals in china clay waste, notably the mica residues, could become the subject of a large integrated mineral processing operation splitting up the waste into its components and extracting the saleable minerals and metals. This is not so far fetched as it might seem, as a large operation doing something similar already exists in the Spruce Pine district of North Carolina, USA. There is also the possibility of lithium extraction as well.

In Cornwall and Devon there will probably be a sustainable business based on low iron, plastic ceramic clays and 'platey' paper filling clays for many years to come, but eventually the china clay industry will contract, but possibly never completely cease. With the abandonment of most of the extractive operations, nature will rapidly take over and I am willing to predict, providing rhododendron scrub and Japanese knotweed are kept under control, that this area could become one of the finest nature reserves in Britain in a few hundred years time, not the least because the varied environments which will create tremendous biodiversity. I can see future members of the China Clay History Society debating the exact function of many of the old plants and buildings that will dot the landscape and recalling the glory days when china clay was king!

ACKNOWLEDGEMENTS

My thanks go to the many people who have made this book possible. Firstly, to the many geologists and other scientists, too numerous to list individually, whose researches have provided information about china clay and it's origin. Dr Robin Shail is thanked for Figure 36 and Mandy Gore of Imerys is thanked for environmental information. Professor Peter Scott is thanked for laboratory work at Camborne School of Mines. The clay compamies Imerys and Goonvean are thanked for their help in locating and transporting the boulders to Wheal Martyn Museum and David Owens, Museum Director, is thanked for his encouragement and assistance in setting up the Boulder Park. My thanks also to my publisher, Charles Thurlow, for seeing through this book project to completion.

FURTHER READING

General Reading

Cornwall's Geology and Scenery, 2nd Edition 2005 by Colin Bristow.
Published by Cornish Hillside Publications.

China clay from Cornwall and Devon, 4th Edition 2005 by Charles Thurlow.
Published by Cornish Hillside Publications.

Specialised Reading

Field Guide to the Cornubian Orefield by A.V. Bromley. Published as part of the
Sixth International Symposium on Water-Rock Interaction, Malvern (UK), 1989,
by the International Association of Geochemistry and Cosmochemistry.

Kaolin Deposits of Europe by C.M. Bristow. Published in the Journal of the
Open University Geological Society in 1992, volume 13, No. 2, pages 2-15.

Igneous Rocks of South-West England by P.A. Floyd, C.S. Exley and M.T. Styles.
Published in 1993 by Chapman and Hall, London as Volume 5 of the Geological
Conservation Review Series. Contains a good review of granite geology and a
detailed description of the granite exposed in the Wheal Martyn Site of Special
Scientific Interest (pages 185-7).

Kaolin Genesis and Utilization. Book with many interesting papers, edited by
Haydn Murray, Wayne Bundy and Colin Harvey, published in 1993 by the Clay
Minerals Society, Boulder, Colorado.

Wealth from the ground, geology and extractive industries by C.M. Bristow 1993.
In 'Cornwall since the war', edited by Philip Payton, published by the Institute of
Cornish Studies/Dyllansow Truran, Redruth.

Historical and Geological Aspects of the China Clay Industry of South-west England, by C.M. Bristow and C.S. Exley. Published in 1994 in the Transactions of
the Royal Geological Society of Cornwall, as Part 6 of Volume 21, pages 247-314.

Industrial clays: kaolin (china clay), ball clay and bentonite by D.A.C. Manning, 1995. Chapter (pages 35-71) in book by D.A.C. Manning entitled 'Introduction to Industrial Minerals', published by Chapman and Hall, London.

The ball clay and china clay industries of Southwest England in 2000, by C.M. Bristow et al. Published in 2002 in 'Industrial Minerals and and Extractive Industry Geology', edited by P.W. Scott and C.M. Bristow, pages 17-41, by The Geological Society, Bath.

The Wheal Martyn Boulder Park, by Colin Bristow and Peter Scott. In Press. To be published in Geoscience in South-west England, volume 11, late 2006. A scientific paper giving details of the chemistry and mineralogy of the boulders.

In addition, articles on kaolin frequently appear in the journal 'Industrial Minerals' and will provide up-to-date information on the latest developments in the kaolin (china clay) industry worldwide.

APPENDIX

List of the boulders at Wheal Martyn (no hammering please!):
1. Biotite granite – Goonbarrow pit
2. China stone – Rostowrack quarry
3. Globular quartz granite – Goonbarrow pit
4. Topaz granite – Treviscoe pit
5. Lithium mica granite – Gunheath pit
6. Pegmatite (stockscheider) – Wheal Martyn pit
7. Elvan – Wheal Remfry pit
8. Quartz-tourmaline vein – Wheal Martyn pit
9. Wheal Remfry breccia – Wheal Remfry pit
10. Schorl with pseudomorphs after feldspar –   Wheal Remfry pit
11. Fluorite on granite – Wheal Martyn pit
12. Lithium mica granite with turquoise and iron staining – Gunheath pit

In addition there is the non-megacrystic Li-mica granite exposed in the SSSI, which is similar to the globular quartz granite of Boulder No. 3. There are also two very fine pillars of coarse grained biotite granite from one of the quarries in the Luxulyan valley on either side of the entrance to the drive up to the former site of Carthew House. This is situated immediately north of the Museum, beside the main road.

INDEX